MATH TRAILBLAZERS™

Grade 3

Transparency Package

Second Edition

A Mathematical Journey Using Science and Language Arts

D1378203

KENDALL/HUNT PUBLISHING COMPANY
4050 Westmark Drive Dubuque, Iowa 52002

A TIMS® Curriculum
University of Illinois at Chicago

This package contains transparencies from the *Unit Resource Guide.* These pages are listed in the Lesson Guide's Material List under "Teacher Materials." Please note that only **Transparencies** from the *Unit Resource Guide* are included, **not** Assessment Blackline Masters or Blackline Masters. This distinction is indicated in the footer on each page. Lesson Guides also often suggest the use of transparencies of activity pages from the *Unit Resource Guide, Student Guide,* or *Discovery Assignment Book.* These recommendations are optional and therefore not included in this package. All pages in the *Blackline Masters: Generic Section* except flash cards are also included at the back of this book.

UIC The University of Illinois at Chicago

The original edition was based on work supported by the National Science Foundation under grant No. MDR 9050226 and the University of Illinois at Chicago. Any opinions, findings, and conclusions or recommendations expressed in this publication are those of the author(s) and do not necessarily reflect the views of the granting agencies.

Cover photo by Design Photography

ISBN 0-7872-8510-2

Printed in the United States of America

2 3 4 5 6 7 8 9 10 07 06 05 04

Table of Contents

Hundreds Template

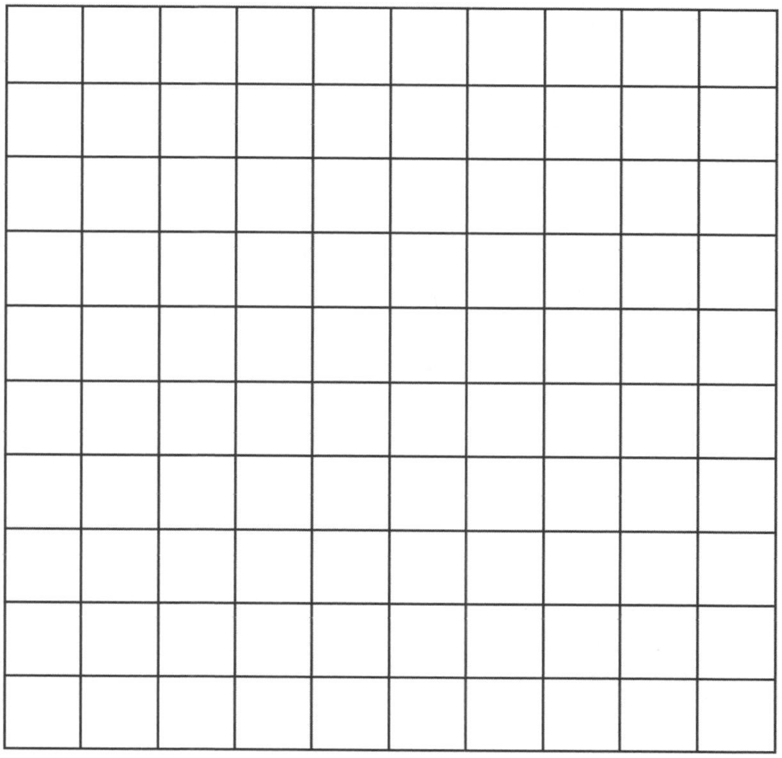

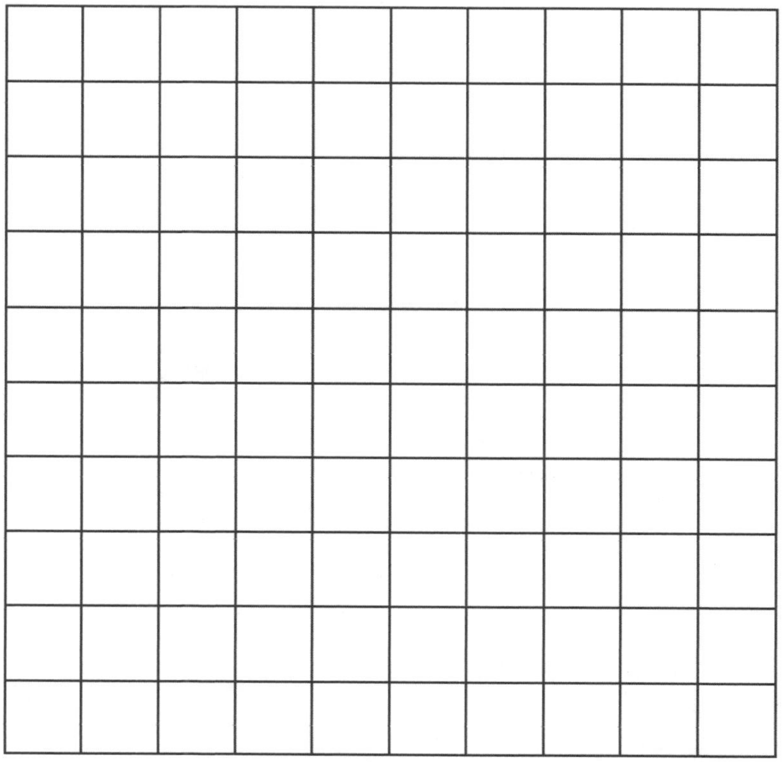

Lemonade Stand Graph

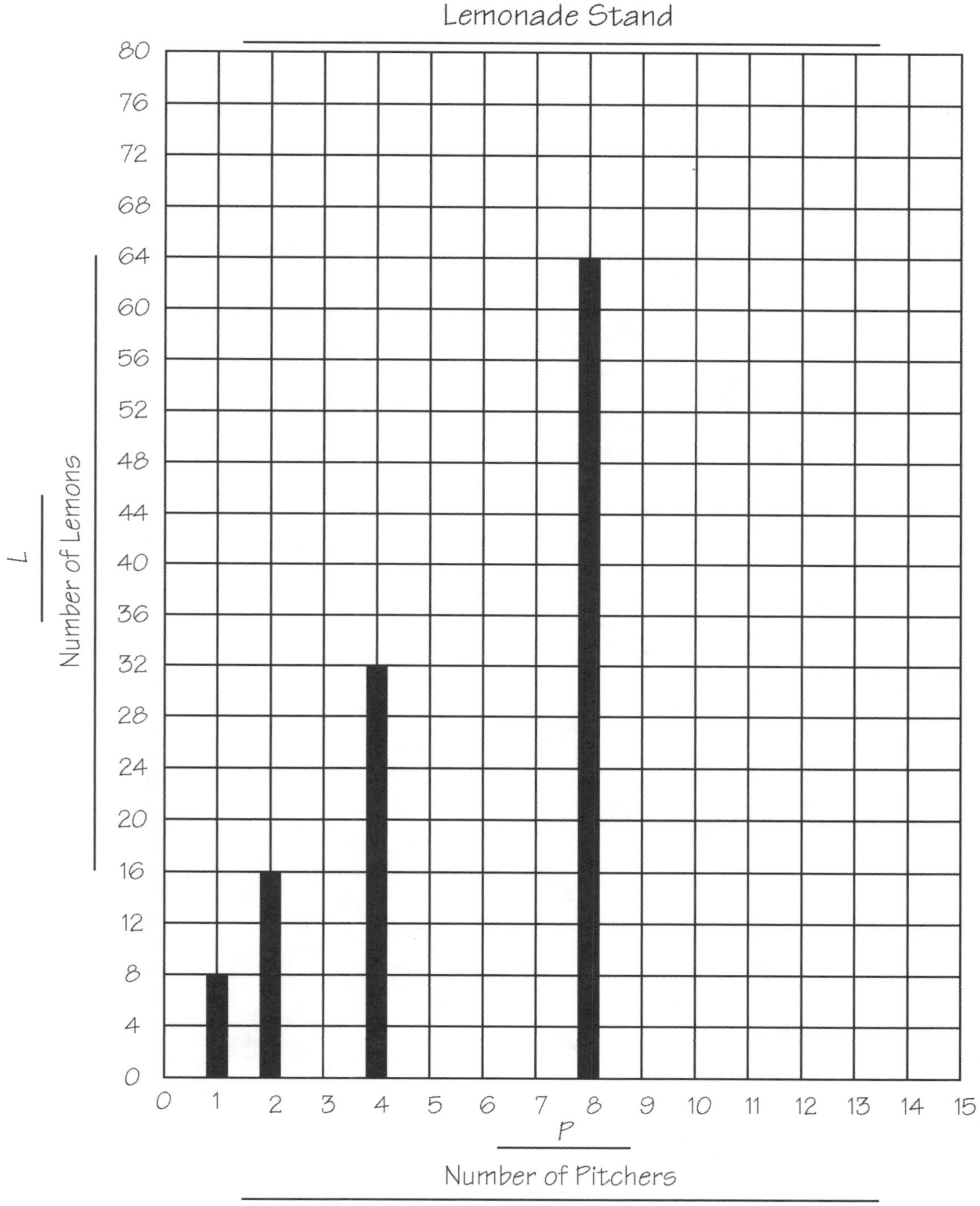

What Went Wrong?

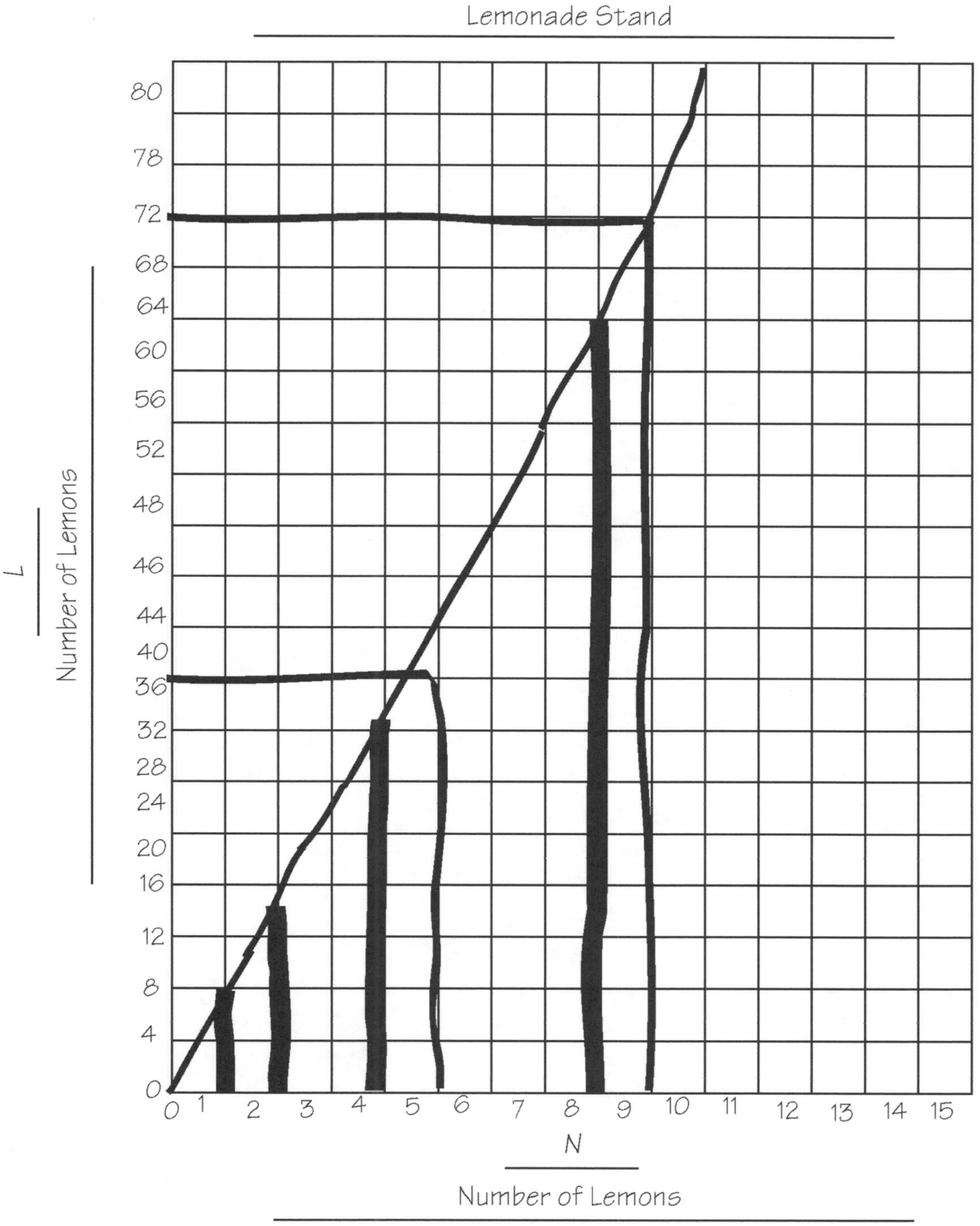
Lemonade Stand
80
78
72
68
64
60
56
52
48
46
44
40
36
32
28
24
20
16
12
8
4
0
L
Number of Lemons
0 1 2 3 4 5 6 7 8 9 10 11 12 13 14 15
N
Number of Lemons

Professor Peabody Travels to the Moon

Professor Peabody knows that **weight** is a measure of the pull of gravity. He decides to travel to the moon to see what happens to his weight and mass.

He discovers that his weight on the moon is less than his Earth weight. This makes him realize that the moon's gravity is weaker than the Earth's. Now, he wants to check his mass.

His mass has stayed the same! **Mass** is the amount of matter in an object. The amount of matter in Prof. Peabody did not change when he went to the moon.

Multiplication Table

×	0	1	2	3	4	5	6	7	8	9	10
0	0	0	0	0	0	0	0	0	0	0	0
1	0	1	2	3	4	5	6	7	8	9	10
2	0	2	4	6	8	10	12	14	16	18	20
3	0	3	6	9	12	15	18	21	24	27	30
4	0	4	8	12	16	20	24	28	32	36	40
5	0	5	10	15	20	25	30	35	40	45	50
6	0	6	12	18	24	30	36	42	48	54	60
7	0	7	14	21	28	35	42	49	56	63	70
8	0	8	16	24	32	40	48	56	64	72	80
9	0	9	18	27	36	45	54	63	72	81	90
10	0	10	20	30	40	50	60	70	80	90	100

Hints for Puzzling Tangrams

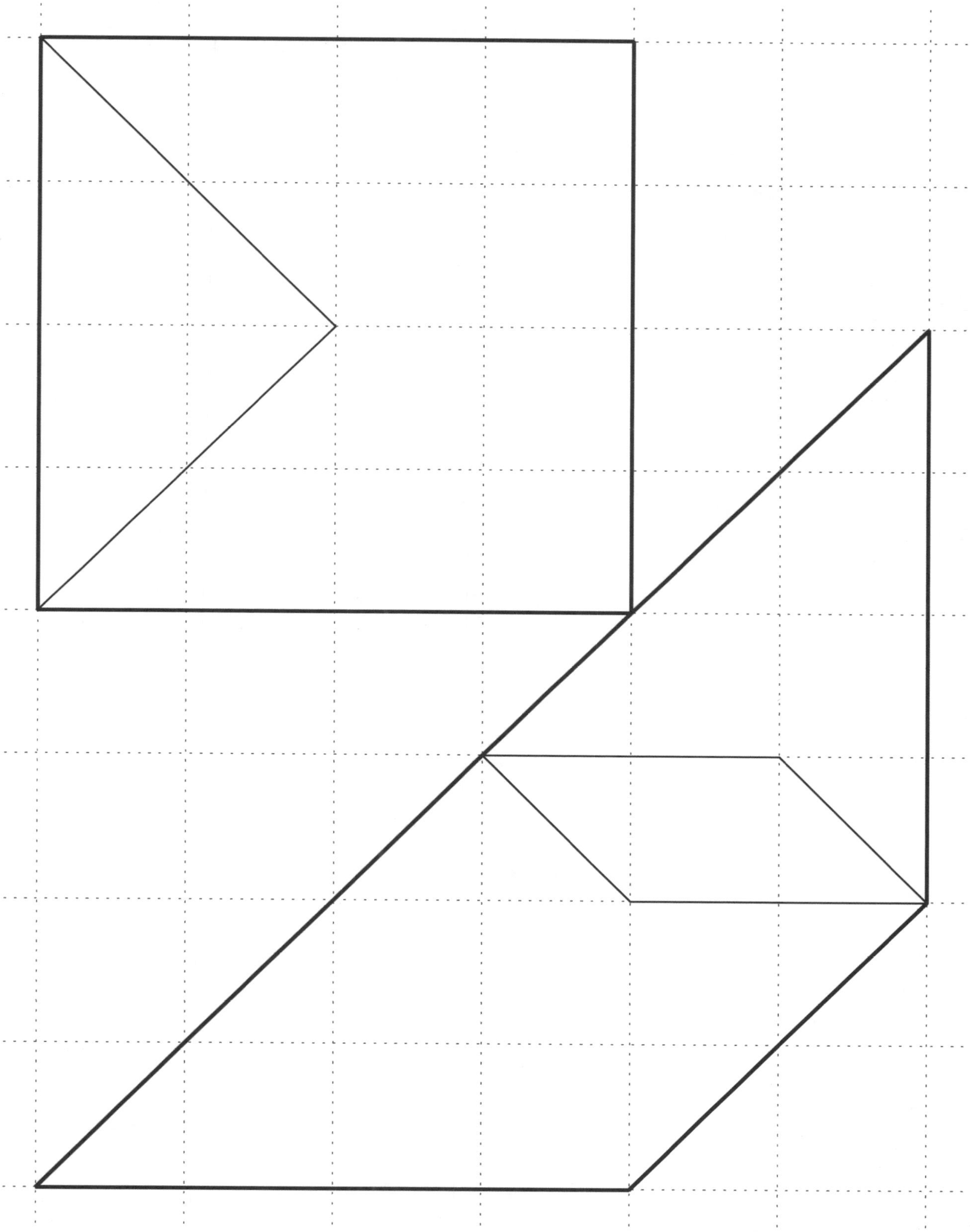

When Are Shapes the Same?

Are these two figures congruent?

4-by-4 Hex

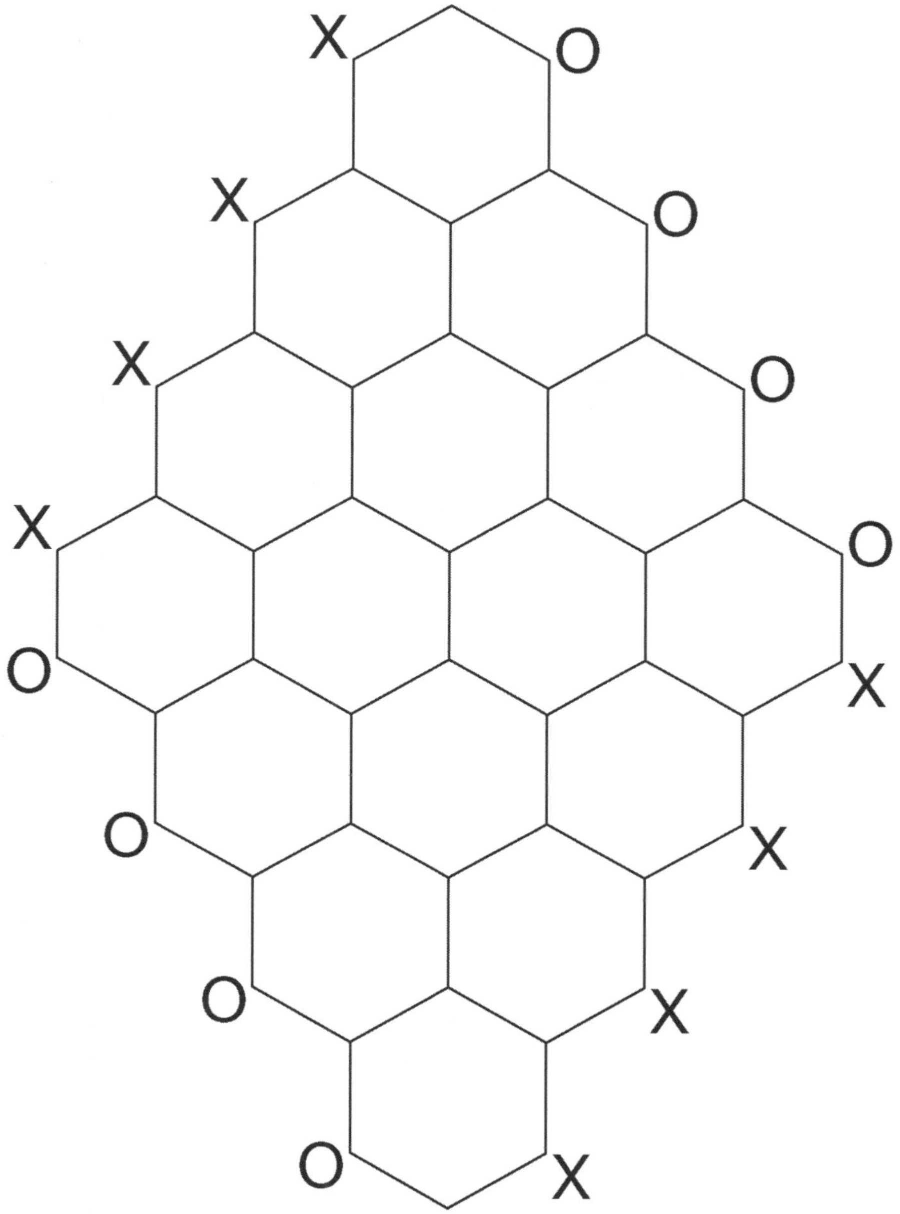

Reading Goal Scale

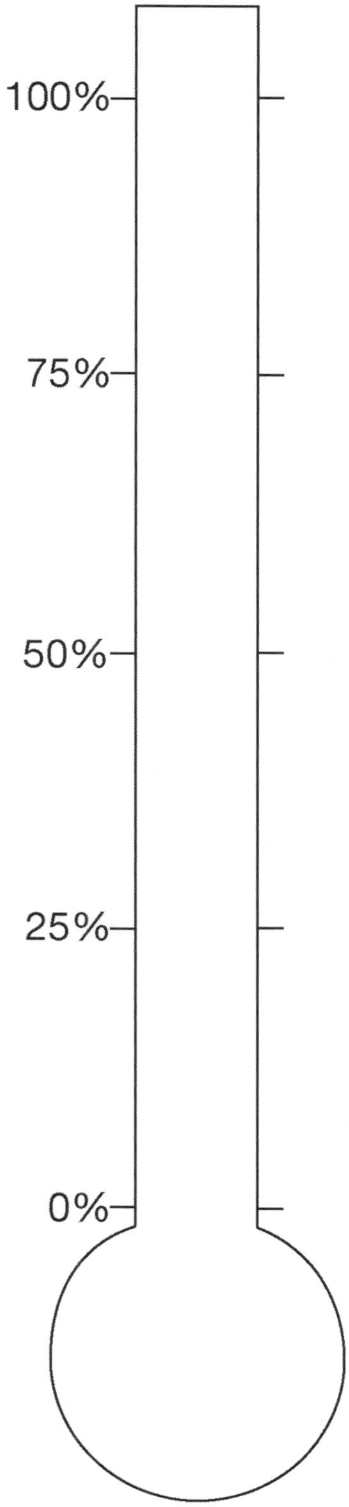

One Whole, Ten Tenths

1

0.1
0.2
0.3
0.4
0.5
0.6
0.7
0.8
0.9
1

Ten Tenths, One Hundred Hundredths

0.1
0.2
0.3
0.4
0.5
0.6
0.7
0.8
0.9
1

0.01	0.02	0.03	0.04	0.05	0.06	0.07	0.08	0.09	0.1
0.11	0.12	0.13	0.14	0.15	0.16	0.17	0.18	0.19	0.2
0.21	0.22	0.23	0.24	0.25	0.26	0.27	0.28	0.29	0.3
0.31	0.32	0.33	0.34	0.35	0.36	0.37	0.38	0.39	0.4
0.41	0.42	0.43	0.44	0.45	0.46	0.47	0.48	0.49	0.5
0.51	0.52	0.53	0.54	0.55	0.56	0.57	0.58	0.59	0.6
0.61	0.62	0.63	0.64	0.65	0.66	0.67	0.68	0.69	0.7
0.71	0.72	0.73	0.74	0.75	0.76	0.77	0.78	0.79	0.8
0.81	0.82	0.83	0.84	0.85	0.86	0.87	0.88	0.89	0.9
0.91	0.92	0.93	0.94	0.95	0.96	0.97	0.98	0.99	1

Scale 1 with Blowup

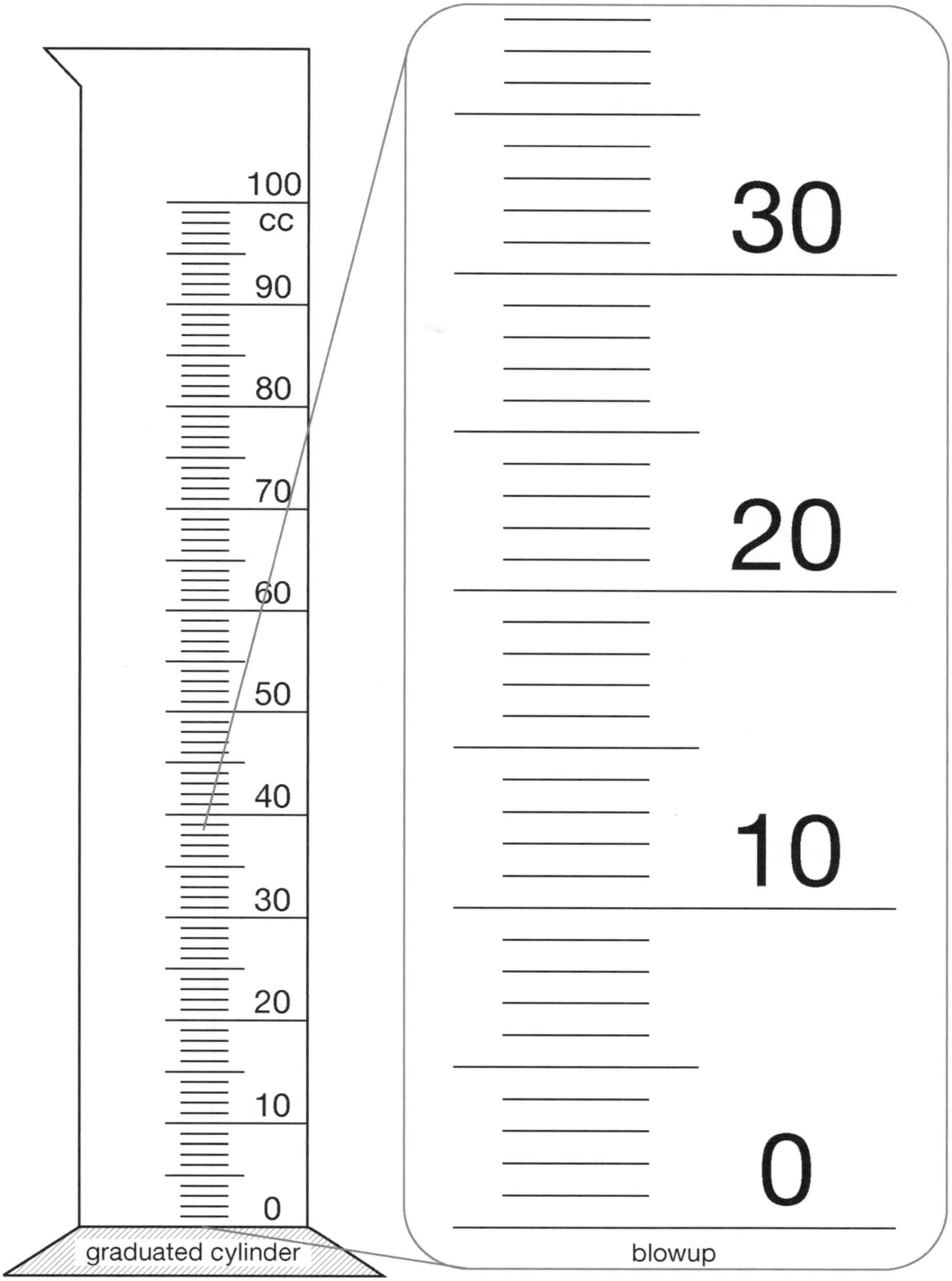

Scale 2 with Blowup

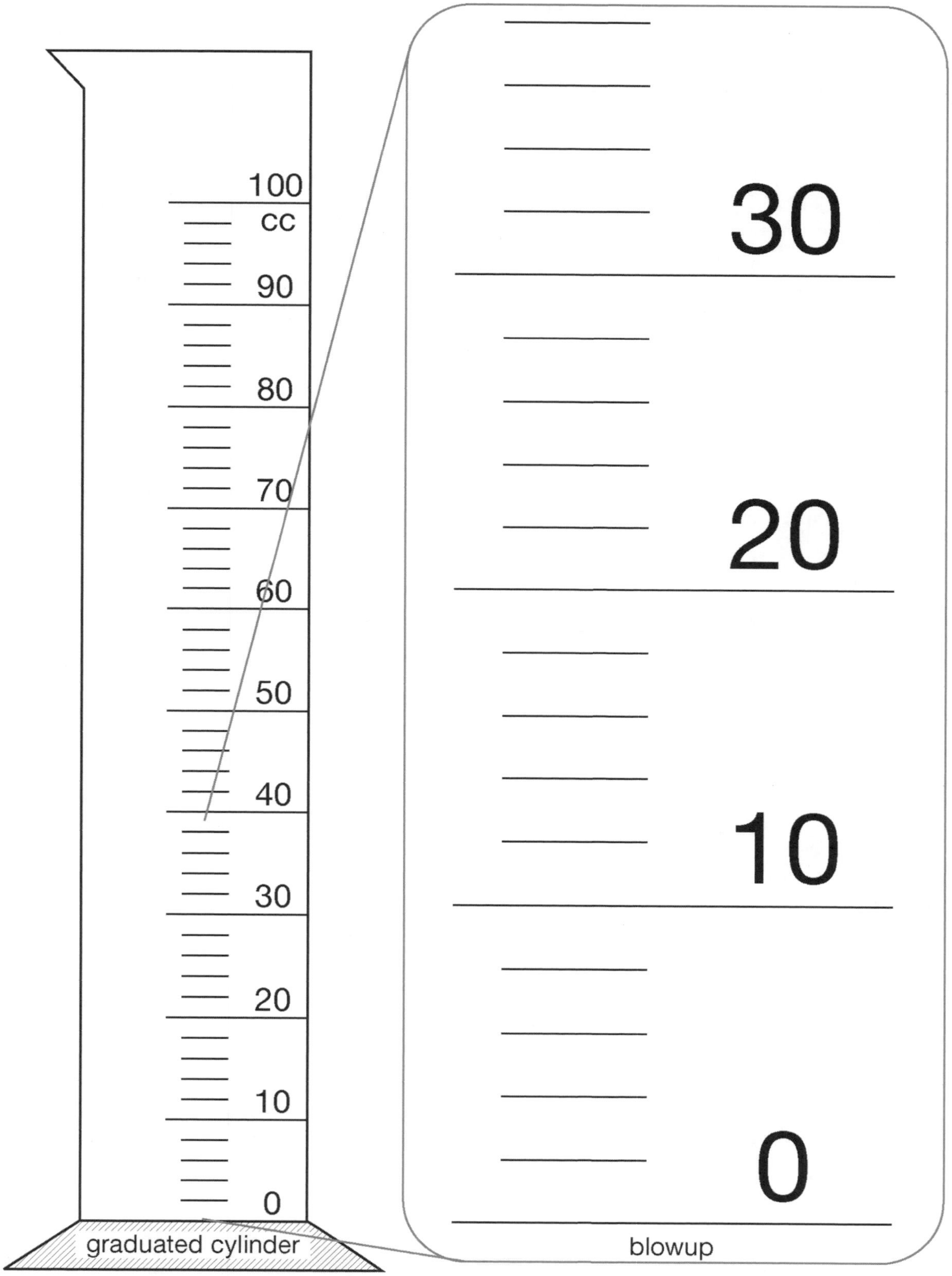

Scale 3 with Blowup

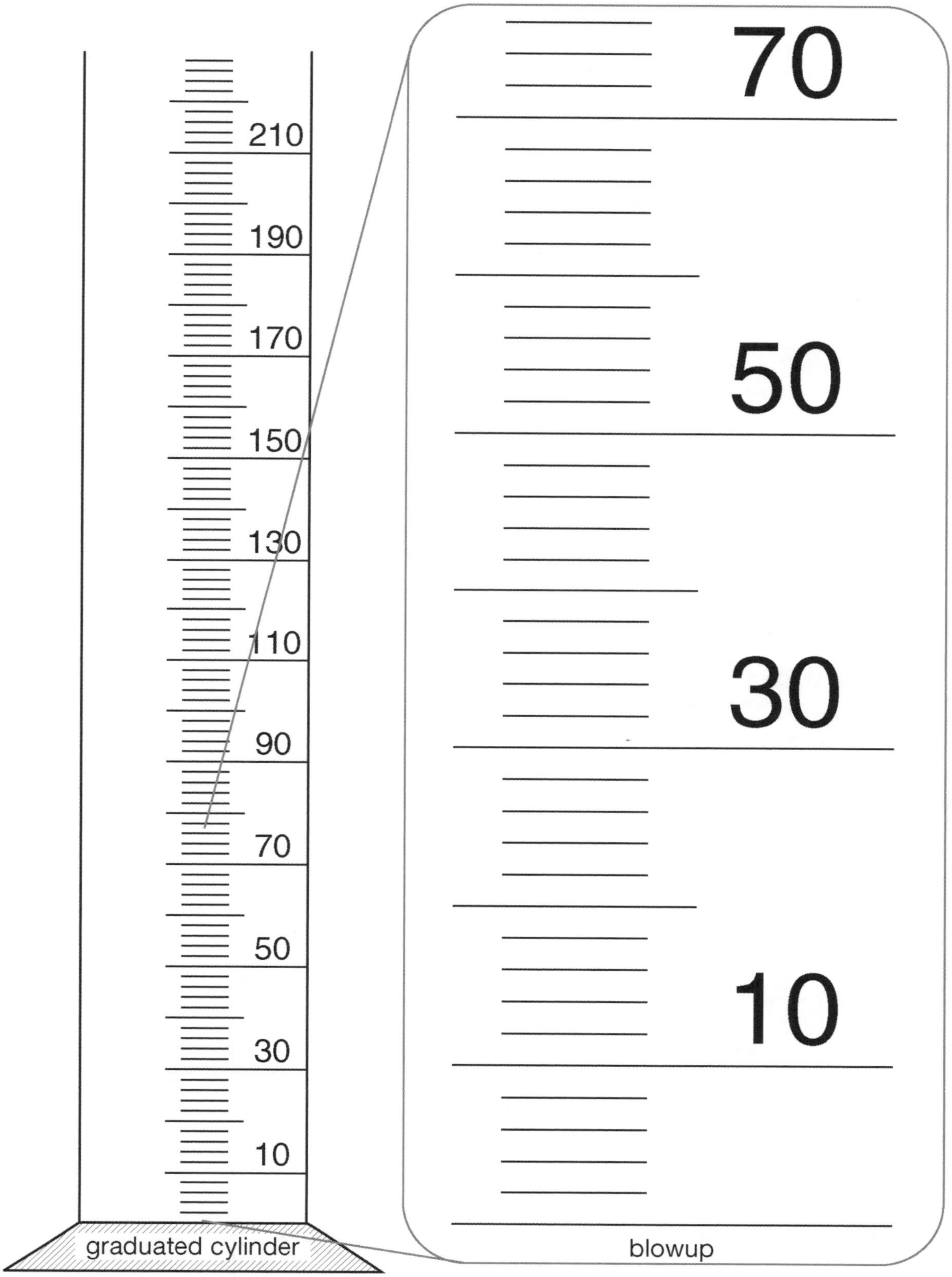

Meniscus

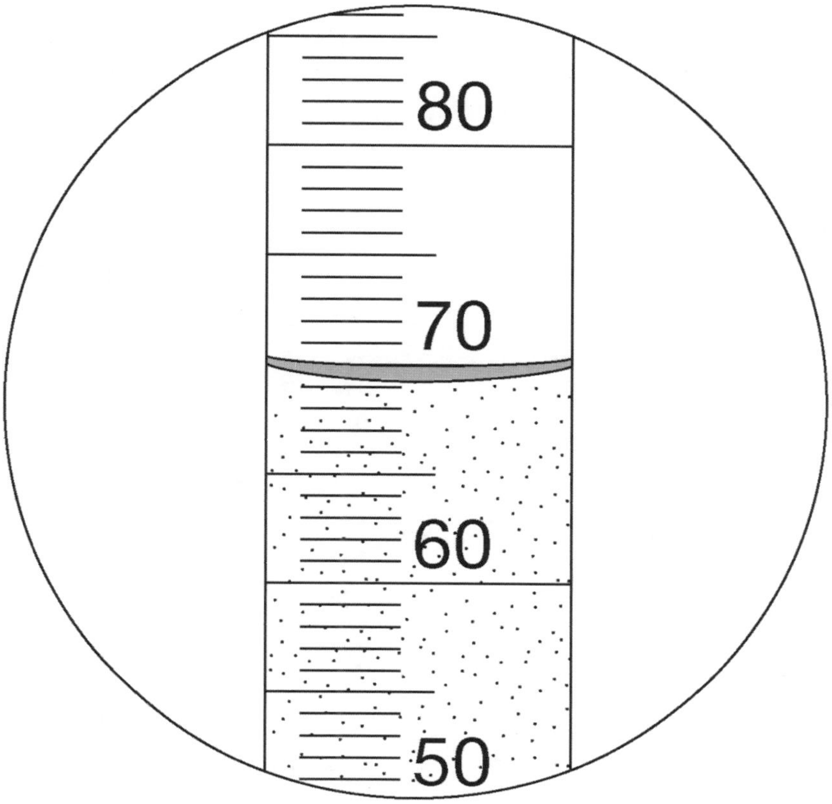

Dee's Cube Model Plan

Back

Left				Right
	2	2	2	
Left	2	2	3	Right

Front

Height = 3 units
Volume = 13 cubic units
Area of Base = 6 square units

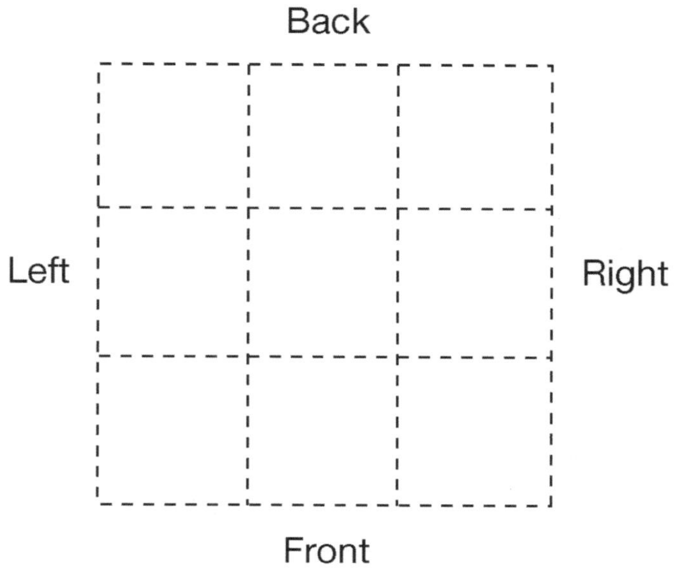

Rectangular Arrays

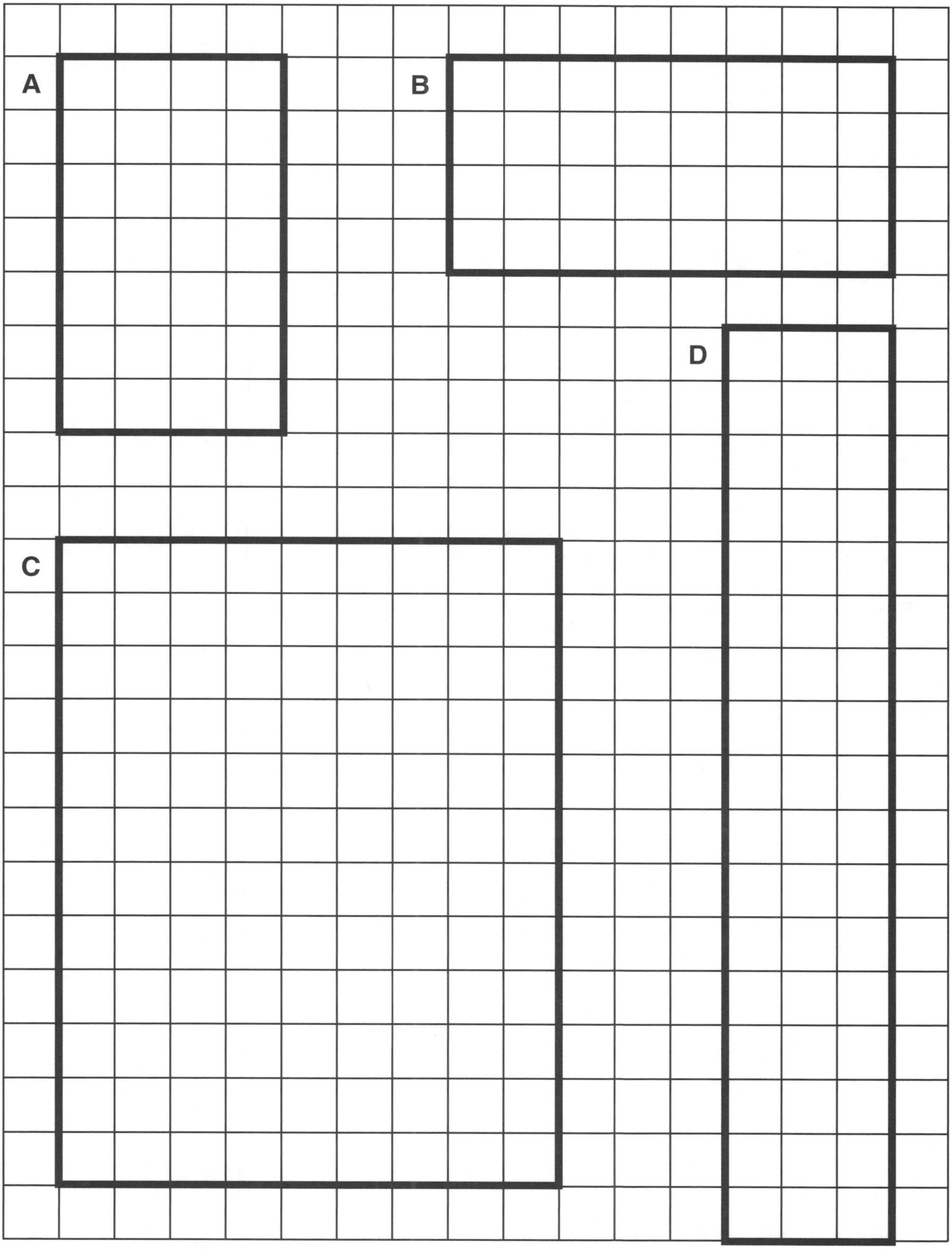

Stencilrama Graph

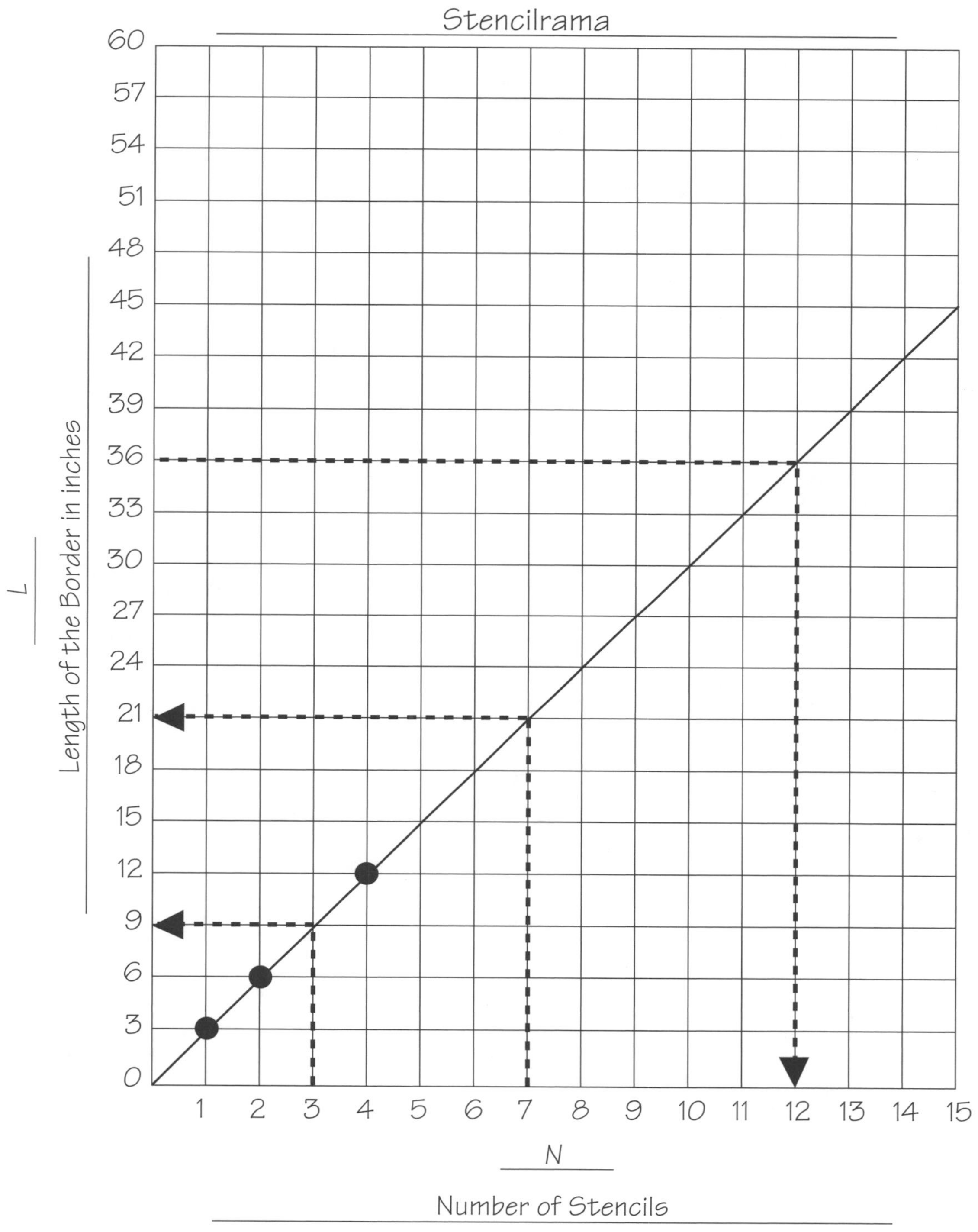

Name ______________________ Date ______________

Spinner 1–4

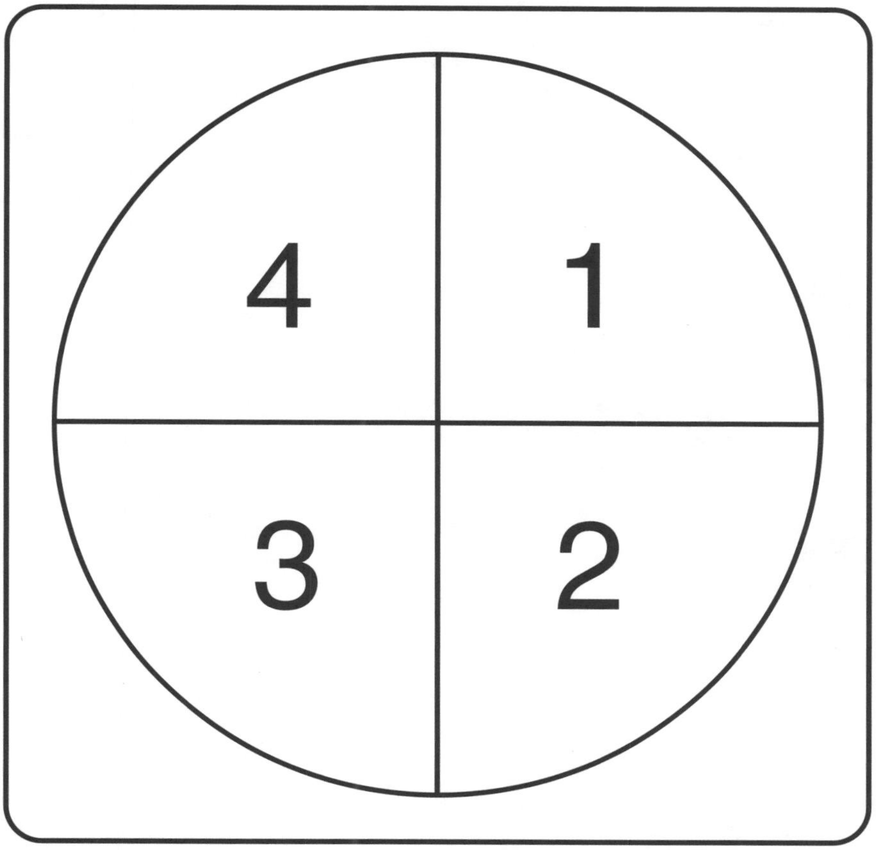

Name ______________________ Date ______________

Spinner 1–10

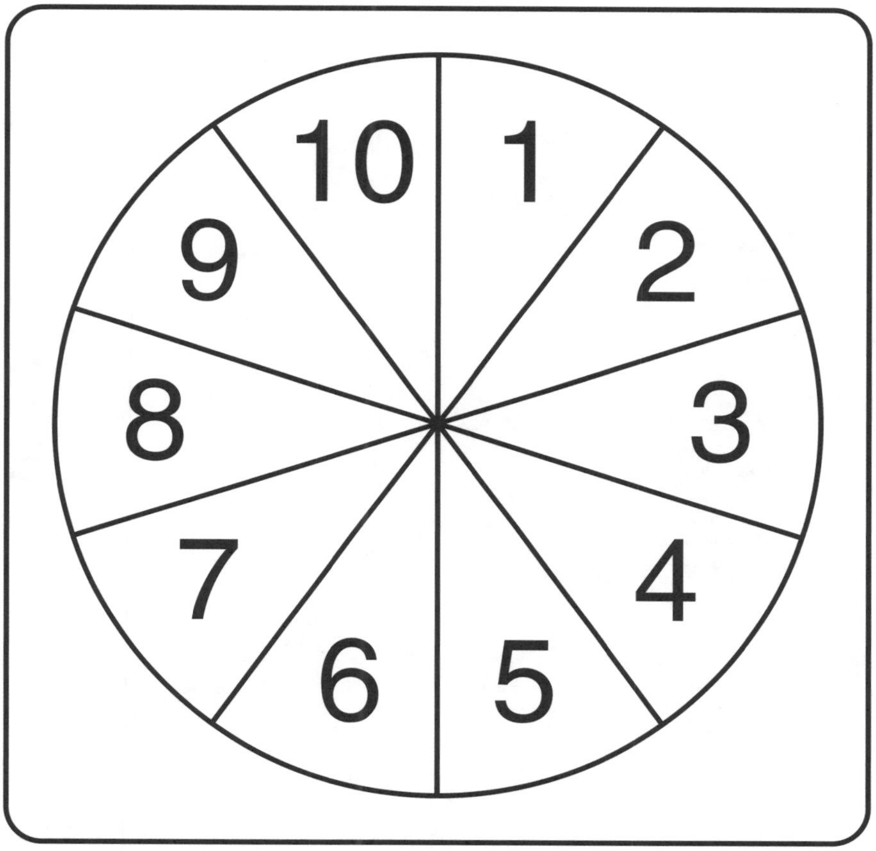

Name ______________________ Date ______________

4	9
3	8
2	7
1	6
0	5

Name ______________________________ Date ________________

5	11
4	10
3	9
2	8
1	7
0	6

Name ______________________________ Date ________________

17	23
16	22
15	21
14	20
13	19
12	18

Name ______________________ Date ______________

100 Chart

1	2	3	4	5	6	7	8	9	10
11	12	13	14	15	16	17	18	19	20
21	22	23	24	25	26	27	28	29	30
31	32	33	34	35	36	37	38	39	40
41	42	43	44	45	46	47	48	49	50
51	52	53	54	55	56	57	58	59	60
61	62	63	64	65	66	67	68	69	70
71	72	73	74	75	76	77	78	79	80
81	82	83	84	85	86	87	88	89	90
91	92	93	94	95	96	97	98	99	100

Name ______________________ Date ______________________

Skinnies	Bits
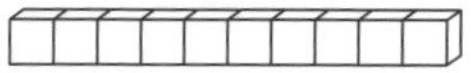	

Name ______________________ Date ______________________

Packs

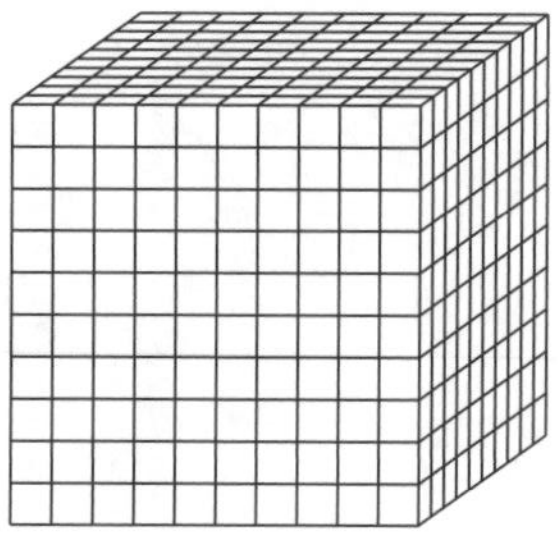

Flats

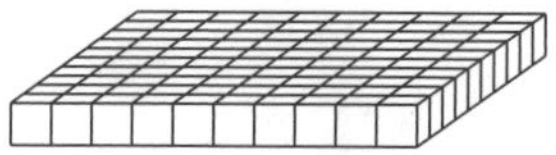

Name ______________________ Date ______________

Base-Ten Pieces Masters

Name ______________________________ Date ______________

Base-Ten Pieces Masters

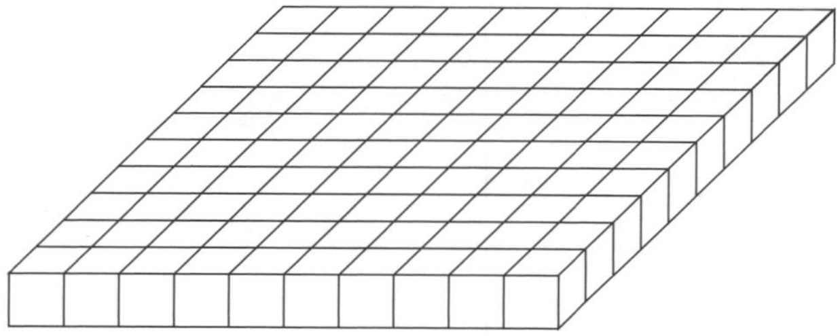

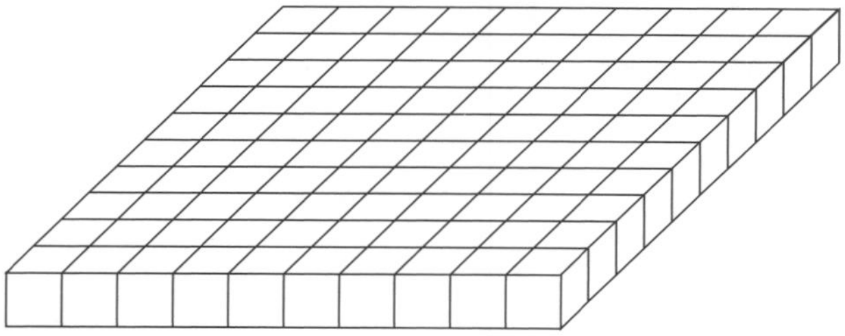

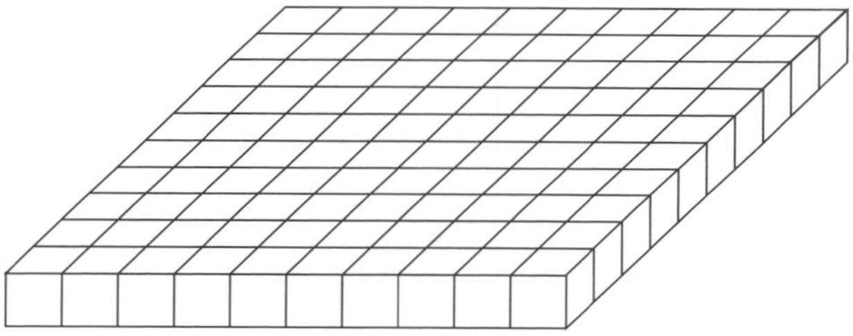

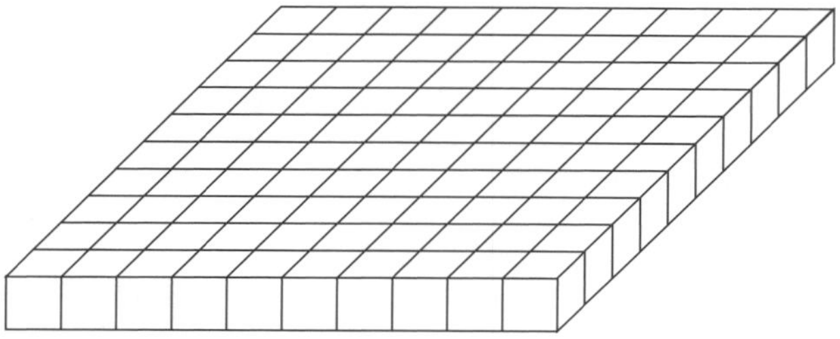

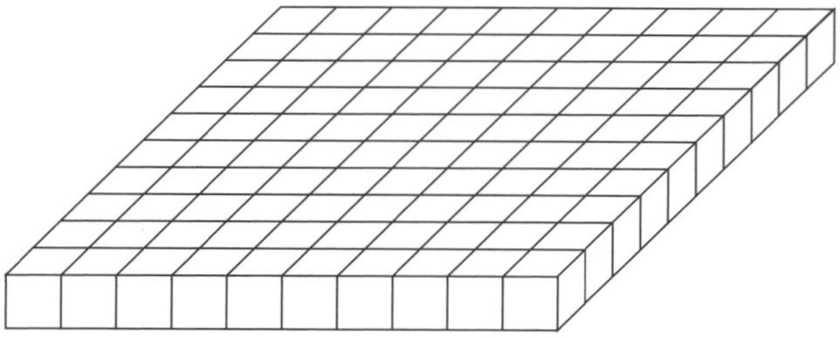

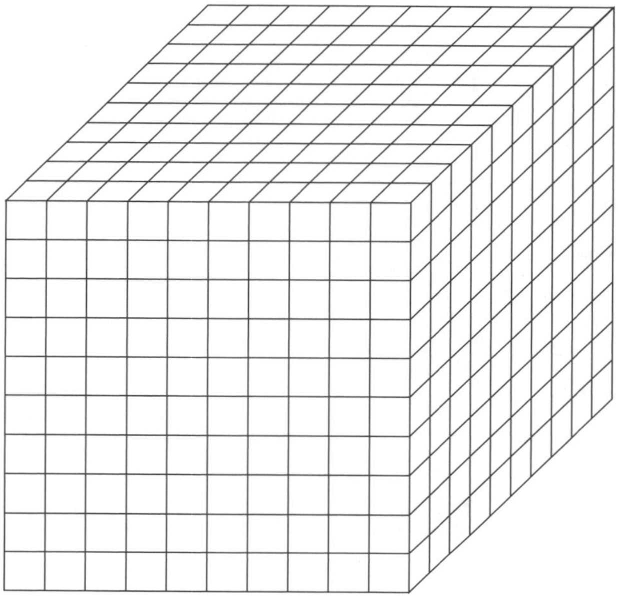

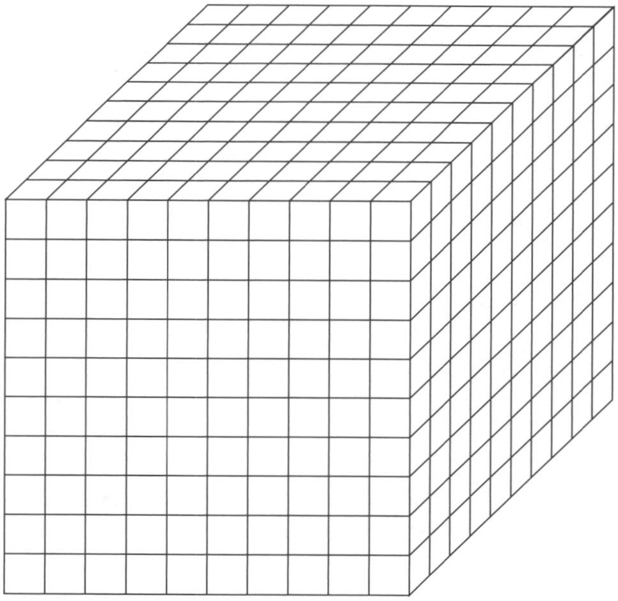

Name ______________________________ Date ______________

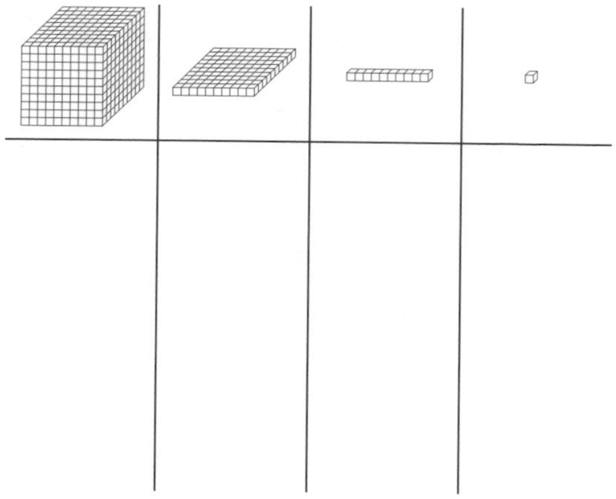

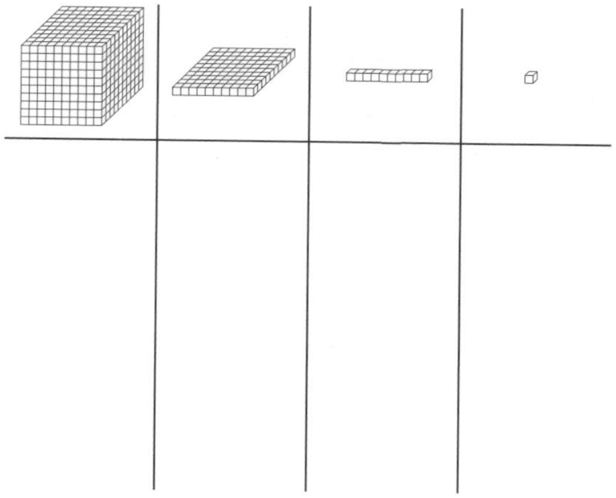

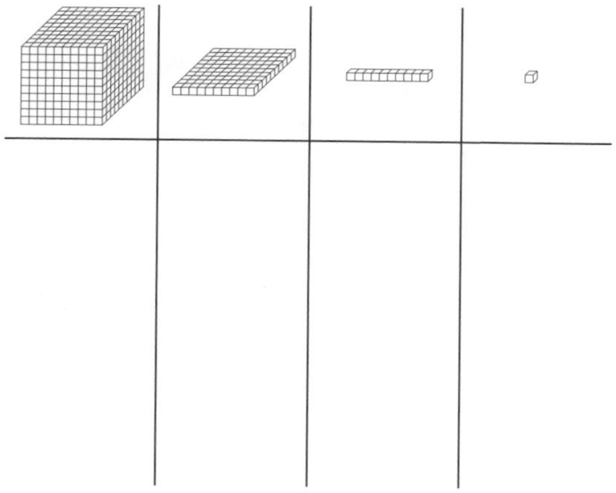

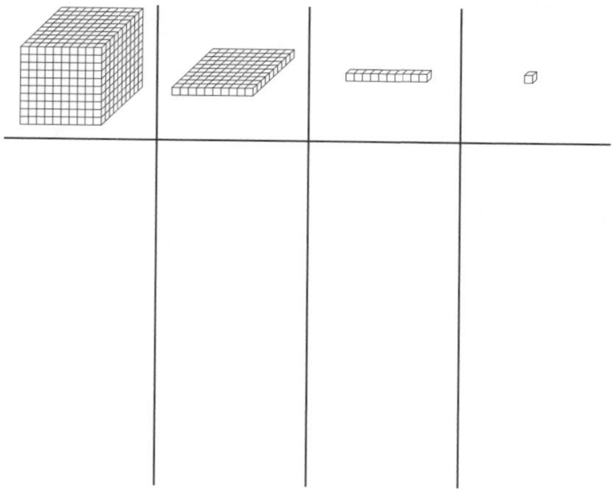

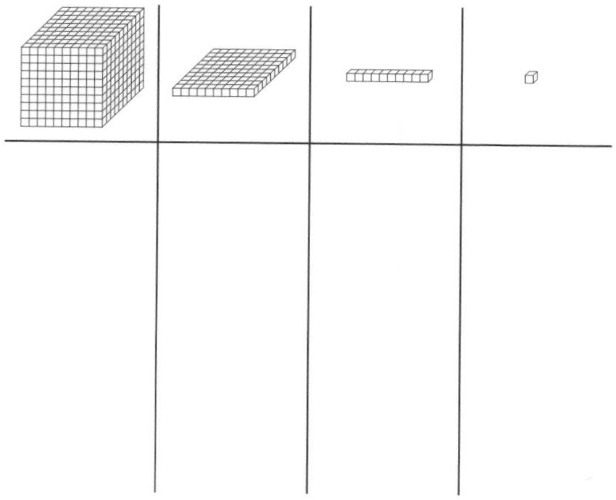

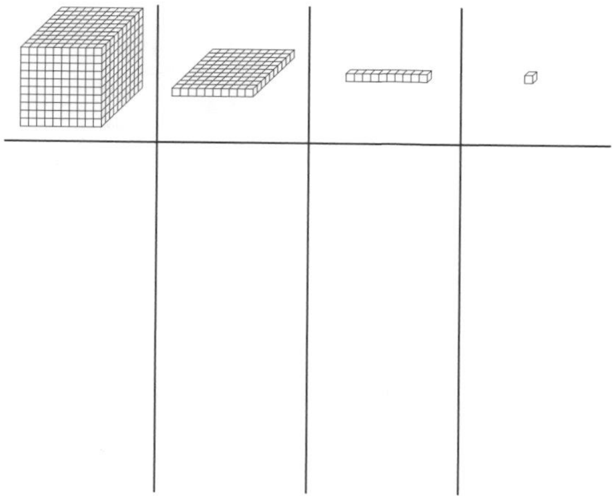

Name ______________________ Date ______________

Name ______________________ Date ______________

Name ______________________ Date ______________

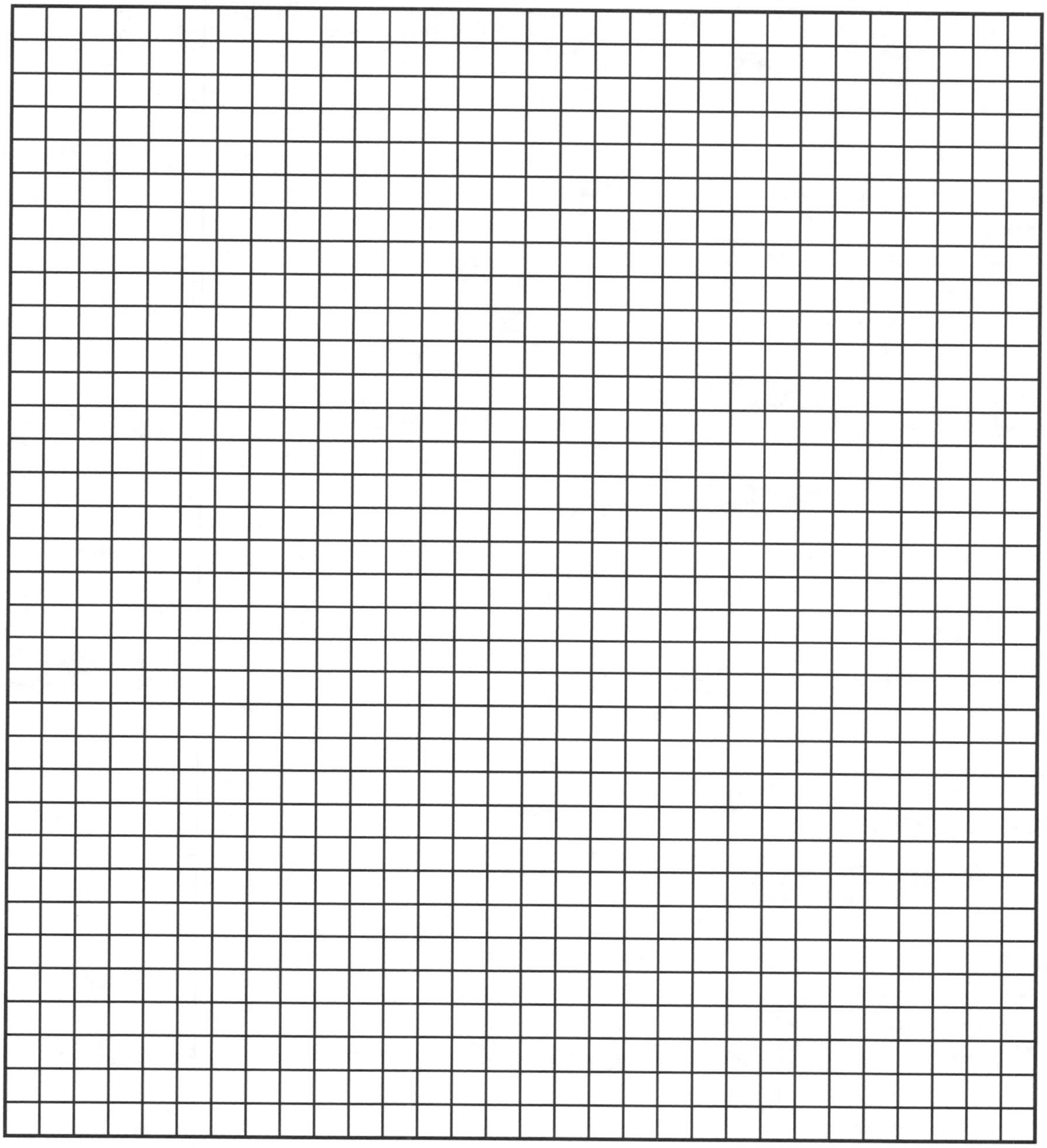

Name ______________________ Date ______________

Name ______________________ Date ______________________

Name ______________________ Date ______________

Name ______________________________ Date ______________

____

Name ______________________ Date ______________

____

Name ______________________________ Date ______________

____

	Trial 1	Trial 2	Trial 3	Average

Name ______________________________ Date ______________

____

Name ______________________ Date ______________

____

Name ______________________________ Date ______________________________

____

Name ______________________ Date ______________

Name ______________________ Date ______________

Subtraction Facts I Know

Circle the subtraction facts you know and can answer quickly.
Underline those facts that you know when you use a strategy.
Do nothing to those facts that you still need to learn.

4 − 2 2	5 − 2 3	6 − 2 4	7 − 2 5	8 − 2 6	9 − 2 7	10 − 2 8	11 − 2 9
5 − 3 2	6 − 3 3	7 − 3 4	8 − 3 5	9 − 3 6	10 − 3 7	11 − 3 8	12 − 3 9
6 − 4 2	7 − 4 3	8 − 4 4	9 − 4 5	10 − 4 6	11 − 4 7	12 − 4 8	13 − 4 9
7 − 5 2	8 − 5 3	9 − 5 4	10 − 5 5	11 − 5 6	12 − 5 7	13 − 5 8	14 − 5 9
8 − 6 2	9 − 6 3	10 − 6 4	11 − 6 5	12 − 6 6	13 − 6 7	14 − 6 8	15 − 6 9
9 − 7 2	10 − 7 3	11 − 7 4	12 − 7 5	13 − 7 6	14 − 7 7	15 − 7 8	16 − 7 9
10 − 8 2	11 − 8 3	12 − 8 4	13 − 8 5	14 − 8 6	15 − 8 7	16 − 8 8	17 − 8 9
11 − 9 2	12 − 9 3	13 − 9 4	14 − 9 5	15 − 9 6	16 − 9 7	17 − 9 8	18 − 9 9
12 − 10 2	13 − 10 3	14 − 10 4	15 − 10 5	16 − 10 6	17 − 10 7	18 − 10 8	19 − 10 9

Name ______________________ Date ______________

Multiplication Facts I Know

- Circle the facts you know well.
- Keep this table and use it to help you multiply.
- As you learn more facts, you may circle them too.

×	0	1	2	3	4	5	6	7	8	9	10
0	0	0	0	0	0	0	0	0	0	0	0
1	0	1	2	3	4	5	6	7	8	9	10
2	0	2	4	6	8	10	12	14	16	18	20
3	0	3	6	9	12	15	18	21	24	27	30
4	0	4	8	12	16	20	24	28	32	36	40
5	0	5	10	15	20	25	30	35	40	45	50
6	0	6	12	18	24	30	36	42	48	54	60
7	0	7	14	21	28	35	42	49	56	63	70
8	0	8	16	24	32	40	48	56	64	72	80
9	0	9	18	27	36	45	54	63	72	81	90
10	0	10	20	30	40	50	60	70	80	90	100

Name ______________________ Date ______________

×	0	1	2	3	4	5	6	7	8	9	10
0	0	0	0	0	0	0	0	0	0	0	0
1	0	1	2	3	4	5	6	7	8	9	10
2	0	2	4	6	8	10	12	14	16	18	20
3	0	3	6	9	12	15	18	21	24	27	30
4	0	4	8	12	16	20	24	28	32	36	40
5	0	5	10	15	20	25	30	35	40	45	50
6	0	6	12	18	24	30	36	42	48	54	60
7	0	7	14	21	28	35	42	49	56	63	70
8	0	8	16	24	32	40	48	56	64	72	80
9	0	9	18	27	36	45	54	63	72	81	90
10	0	10	20	30	40	50	60	70	80	90	100

×	0	1	2	3	4	5	6	7	8	9	10
0	0	0	0	0	0	0	0	0	0	0	0
1	0	1	2	3	4	5	6	7	8	9	10
2	0	2	4	6	8	10	12	14	16	18	20
3	0	3	6	9	12	15	18	21	24	27	30
4	0	4	8	12	16	20	24	28	32	36	40
5	0	5	10	15	20	25	30	35	40	45	50
6	0	6	12	18	24	30	36	42	48	54	60
7	0	7	14	21	28	35	42	49	56	63	70
8	0	8	16	24	32	40	48	56	64	72	80
9	0	9	18	27	36	45	54	63	72	81	90
10	0	10	20	30	40	50	60	70	80	90	100

×	0	1	2	3	4	5	6	7	8	9	10
0	0	0	0	0	0	0	0	0	0	0	0
1	0	1	2	3	4	5	6	7	8	9	10
2	0	2	4	6	8	10	12	14	16	18	20
3	0	3	6	9	12	15	18	21	24	27	30
4	0	4	8	12	16	20	24	28	32	36	40
5	0	5	10	15	20	25	30	35	40	45	50
6	0	6	12	18	24	30	36	42	48	54	60
7	0	7	14	21	28	35	42	49	56	63	70
8	0	8	16	24	32	40	48	56	64	72	80
9	0	9	18	27	36	45	54	63	72	81	90
10	0	10	20	30	40	50	60	70	80	90	100

×	0	1	2	3	4	5	6	7	8	9	10
0	0	0	0	0	0	0	0	0	0	0	0
1	0	1	2	3	4	5	6	7	8	9	10
2	0	2	4	6	8	10	12	14	16	18	20
3	0	3	6	9	12	15	18	21	24	27	30
4	0	4	8	12	16	20	24	28	32	36	40
5	0	5	10	15	20	25	30	35	40	45	50
6	0	6	12	18	24	30	36	42	48	54	60
7	0	7	14	21	28	35	42	49	56	63	70
8	0	8	16	24	32	40	48	56	64	72	80
9	0	9	18	27	36	45	54	63	72	81	90
10	0	10	20	30	40	50	60	70	80	90	100

Name ______________________ Date ______________________

Sorting Flash Cards

Problems Answered Correctly and Quickly	Problems Answered Correctly after Thinking	Problems Answered Incorrectly